Edie Shear '99

M000239321

The Charlton Price Guide To

ROYAL WORCESTER FIGURINES

Models by Freda Doughty

First Edition

By
Anthony Cast
John Edwards

W. K. Cross
Publisher

The Charlton Press

Birmingham, Michigan ● Toronto, Ontario

COPYRIGHT NOTICE AND TRADEMARK NOTICE

Copyright © 1997 Charlton International Inc. All Rights Reserved.

Photographs © Charlton International Inc.

The terms Charlton, Charlton's, The Charlton Press and abbreviations thereof, are trademarks of Charlton International Inc. and shall not be used without written consent from Charlton International Inc.

The word Worcester is a registered trademark of The Worcester Royal Porcelain Company Limited and is used herein to express items of collector interest.

While every care has been taken to ensure accuracy in the compilation of the data in this guide, the publisher cannot accept responsibility for typographical errors.

No part of this publication, except the various numbering systems, may be reproduced, stored in a retrieval system, or transmitted in any form or by any means, electronic, mechanical, photocopying, recording, or otherwise, without the prior written permission of the copyright owner.

No copyright material may be used without written permission in each instance from Charlton International Inc. Permission is hereby given for brief excerpts to be used in newspapers, magazines, periodicals and bulletins, other than in the advertising of items for sale, providing the source of the material so used is acknowledged in each instance.

DISCLAIMER

Products listed or shown were manufactured by The Worcester Royal Porcelain Company Limited. This book has been produced independently and neither the authors nor the publisher has any connection whatsoever with The Worcester Royal Porcelain Company Limited.

The Charlton price guide to Royal Worcester figurines

Biennial.
1st ed.
"Models by Freda Doughty".
ISSN 1208-9249
ISBN 0-88968-159-7 (1997 ed.)

    1. Doughty, Freda—Catalogs. 2. Royal Worcester figurines—Catalogs.

NK4660.C49   738'.092   C97-900093-9

EDITORIAL

Editor	Jean Dale
Editorial Assistant	Nicola Leedham
Graphic Technician	Davina Rowan
Photography	Anthony Cast

ACKNOWLEDGEMENTS

The Charlton Press would like to thank all those who have helped with the first edition of The Charlton Price Guide to Royal Worcester Figures; Models by Freda Doughty.

A SPECIAL NOTE TO COLLECTORS

The Charlton Press has an ongoing commitment to excellence and completeness in the production of all its reference works. Your help in providing new or previously unobtainable data on any aspect of Royal Worcester will be considered for inclusion in subsequent editions. Those providing information will be acknowledged in the contributor's section of this catalogue.

Please send your contributions together with your name, address and phone number to our editorial offices in Toronto:

The Charlton Press

Editorial Office:
2040 Yonge Street, Suite 208
Toronto, Ontario M4S 1Z9
Telephone: (416) 488-1418 Fax: (416) 488-4653
Telephone: (800) 442-6042 Fax: (800) 442-1542

Printed in Canada
in the Province of Quebec

HOW TO USE THIS PRICE GUIDE

THE PURPOSE

As with the other catalogues in Charlton's collector reference and pricing library, this publication has been designed to serve two specific purposes. First, to furnish the collector with accurate and detailed listings that provide the essential information needed to build a rewarding collection. Second, to provide collectors and dealers with current market prices.

STYLES AND VERSIONS

STYLES — A change in style occurs when a major element of the design is altered or modified as a result of a deliberate mould change. An example of this is The Duchess's Dress (3106).

VERSIONS — Versions are modifications in a minor style element, such as Grandmother's Dress (3081).

VARIATIONS — A change in colour is a variation.

THE LISTINGS

The figures are arranged numerically according to the Royal Worcester model number assigned to the figurine. Miniature figures were not assigned model numbers and are therefore listed with their respective original versions.

All of the listings include height, colour, and colour variations, dates of issue and discontinuance, varieties and series.

A WORD ON PRICING

The purpose of this catalogue is to give readers the most accurate, up-to-date retail prices in United States and Canadian dollars and British pounds for figures designed by Freda Doughty for Royal Worcester.

To accomplish this, The Charlton Press continues to access an international pricing panel of experts who submit prices based on both dealer and collector retail-price activity, as well as current auction results in the U. S., Canadian and the U. K. markets. These market prices are carefully averaged to reflect accurate valuations for figures in each of these markets. All discontinued figures are priced in this manner.

Current figures are priced according to the manufacturer's suggested retail price. Please be aware that price or promotional sales discounting is always possible and can result in lower prices than those listed.

The prices published herein are for figures in mint condition. Collectors are cautioned that a repaired or restored piece may be worth as little as 50 percent of the value of the same figure in mint condition.

A further word on pricing. As mentioned previously, this is a catalogue giving prices for figures in the currency of a particular market (U.S. dollars for the American market and sterling for the U.K. market). The bulk of the prices given herein are not determined by currency exchange calculations, but by actual market activity in the market concerned

Additionally, collectors must remember that all relevant information must be known to make a proper valuation of price. When comparing auction prices to catalogue prices, collectors and dealers must remember two important points. First, compare "apples and apples." Be sure that auction prices realized for figures include a buyer's premium if one is due. Buyer's premiums can range from 10 to 15 percent, and on an expensive piece this amount can be substantial. Secondly, know whether a figure is restored, repaired or in mint condition. This fact may not be noted or explained in the listings, and as a result, its price will not be reflective of that same piece in mint condition. Please be aware of repairs and restorations and the effect they may have on values.

A last word of caution. No pricing catalogue can be, or should be, a fixed price list. This catalogue must be considered a pricing guide only—showing the most current retail prices based on market demand within a particular region for the various figures.

TABLE OF CONTENTS

In 1751 The Worcester Porcelain Company was founded by Dr. John Wall and a group of local businessmen. Together with William Davis, an apothecary, Dr. Wall developed a formula for making a procelain which didn't crack or craze. This newly formed company leased their first premises, Warmstry House, in Worcester. Their next venture was the purchase of the Miller and Lund soft-paste factory in Bristol.

While The Worcester Porcelain Company's main area of concentration was on the production of serviceable wares and fine tea services, they did make a handful of figures in their early years. It was at the Lund factory that the first porcelain figure, a white glazed standing Chinaman, was made. It wasn't until 1757 that a porcelain figure was made at the Worcester factory. "Cupid at Vulcan's Forge" was probably modelled by John Toulouse who also modelled the Chelsea figures of this same period. Toulouse occasionally signed his moulds "T," "TO," or "IT."

Dr. Wall died in 1776 and the firm was purchased by the company's London agent, Thomas Flight. Flight, together with his sons John and Joseph and various other family members, ran the Worcester factory until the 1840s. At this time they merged with another Worcester company that had been formed by a former employee, Robert Chamberlain. In 1852 the company was purchased by W. H. Kerr and R. W. Binns.

These two men introduced parian (a durable material with a high felspar content) to the Worcester factory. Parian, which was perfect for detailed modelling, was also gilded and enamelled with ease. Up until the 1920s virtually all of Worcester's figures were produced in parian. Binns and Kerr also recognized the importance of the modeller. The company hired trained sculptors to work on their models. The three principal modellers in the 1850s and 1860s were, W. B. Kirk, E. J. Jones and Charles Toft. In the 1870s it was James Hadley who produced the greatest number and variety of Worcester models. Hadley's best known works are his Middle Eastern subjects, the Water Carriers and the set of figures which comprise the Countries of the World series. One of his finest pupils was Charles Noke who left Worcester for Doulton in 1899. Doulton was one of Worcester's greatest figure-making rivals. Hadley himself left Worcester in 1896 to form his own business with his sons. Hadley died in 1903 and two years later his business was acquired by the Worcester Royal Porcelain Company.

It was at this time that an important legal battle was fought over the Worcester name. A Worcester firm, Locke & Co., were using the word Worcester on their pieces. The courts ruled that "Worcester" could only be used to describe products manufactured by the Worcester Royal Porcelain Company.

The turn of the century found Worcester producing figures modelled by George Evans and his sons Ernest and Sydney who had been trained by Hadley. Around 1910, George Evans modelled a tiny tortoise which proved to be an immense success for the factory. This inspired Worcester to bring out a series of small birds, fish and animals. The most popular of these series were the Rabbit (1607) and the Mouse (2610), both of which remained in production until the 1950s.

The years of the First World War saw the Worcester factory producing delicate porcelain figures in a style reminiscent of German crinolines. The Historical and Regimental series, modelled by Frederick Gertner, were also introduced at this time. Gertner also modelled a range of small nude figures of boys and girls in Crownware. Crownware (a high-fired earthenware) was much cheaper to produce that parian. This proved, however, to be an unsuccessful move for the Worcester factory. Worcester tried to branch out by producing powder bowls, ashtrays and toby jugs. Nothing however could prevent the factory from going into receivership on July 24, 1930. Its doors were closed the following day.

Two weeks later the factory reopened under the direction of Joseph Grimson. The next few years found the Worcester factory producing ninety new figures. Grimson then brought in a group of new sculptors from London. Some of Worcester's most successful modellers over the next decades were Stella Crofts, Dorothy and Freda Doughty, Doris Linder, Gwendolyn Parnell, Agnes Pinder-Davis, Ronald and Ruth Van Ruyckevelt, Eva Soper and Pheobe Stabler.

BACKSTAMPS

DATING

With Freda Doughty arriving at the Worcester factory in 1930, the task of dating her figurines, when taken in context for dating Royal Worcester porcelain in general, are simple.

Only two different colour backstamps were used.

The Puce Marks 1925 - 1940

1930	Three horizontal lines
1931	OO (two circles)
1932	OOO (three circles)
1933 to	Three circles and one
1939	dot for each year

The Black Marks 1938 to date

B-1	1938	Three circles and 6 dots
	1939	Three circles and 7 dots
	1940	Three circles and 8 dots
		A blue wavy line was added for 1938, 1939 and 1940
B-2	1941 to	Three circles and 9 dots
	1942	Three circles and 10 dots

1943 to	The black mark with
1948	no date code

B-3	1949	Black mark with V

B-4	1950	Black mark with W
	1951 to	Black mark with W and one
	1961	dot for each added year

B-5	1962	Black mark with ®
	1963 to 1972	Black mark which may or may not have dots added for years
	1973 to 1993	Black mark with ® but no dots
B-6	1994 to date	Black mark with a R within a diamond

FREDA G. DOUGHTY

Freda Doughty came from an accomplished artistic family. Her father Charles, whose major work "Arabia Deserta" was the nucleus of Lawrence of Arabia, was a renowned poet; her mother was a talented painter; and her elder sister, Dorothy, was a sculptress and fellow Worcester modeller.

Freda and Dorothy were taken on by the Worcester factory in the 1930s. Nature was Dorothy's chosen realm and her interpretations of John James Audubon's ornithological sketches are amongst Worcester's most collected pieces. Freda's association with the Worcester factory came about almost by fluke. One of the companies directors, Colonel Clive, was staying with the Doughty's cousin when he saw four pieces that Freda has sculptered. These four models (2912-2915) became Freda's first series Michael, Tommy, Mischief and Joan. While Dorothy concentrated on Limited Editions of flowers and birds, Freda devoted herself to detailed studies of children.

As Freda was unmarried, most of the children she modelled were neighbours of the Doughty's in Kent. The children did not officially sit for the modelling, Freda captured them in play which explains the innocence and naturalness of her pieces. The Doughty's Kent garden bird bath was the model for "Sunshine" (3083).

The Children of the Nations series was introduced in 1934. The initial ten models were numbered 3066 to 2075. Wales (3103) and Scotland (3104) were produced in 1935 and Ireland (3178), the last figure in the series, was introduced in 1936. India, China and Burmah continued to be made until the 1970s.

In 1935 her two best-selling figures, Grandmother's Dress (3081) and Boy With Parakeet (3087), were launched. Three years later the Days of the Week series, based on the popular nursery rhyme, was made available. Miniature versions of these figures were introduced in the 1980s.

Doughty was asked to produce a series of models to represent each month of the year. These delightful figures were in production from the late 1940s until 1985.

The seven models which comprise the Alice in Wonderland series (3608-3614) were not as popular from the onset as her other models. These figures are more often found in the United States than in the United Kingdom, indicating perhaps that they were intended for export.

Freda and her sister had moved to Falmouth, Devon in 1943. It is here they spent their retirement years. Dorothy died in 1962 following a fall, and Freda died ten years later. Their contribution to the success of Worcester figures is unrivaled.

2912   *MICHAEL*

SERIES: *Michael, Tommy, Mischief and Joan*

Modeller:	Freda Doughty
Colourways:	**A.** Blue suit with yellow highlights; yellow hair; blue, green and beige base
	B. Green suit; yellow hair; green and beige base
	C. Red suit with yellow highlights; yellow hair; green and beige base
	D. Yellow suit with lemon highlights; yellow hair; green and beige base
Backstamp:	**1.** Puce
	2. Black

R.W. No.	Backstamp	Height	Intro.	Discon.	Current Market Value U.K. £	Current Market Value U.S. $	Current Market Value Can. $
2912	Puce	2 1/2"	1931	1940	225.00	350.00	475.00
2912	B-2 to B-4	2 1/2"	1940	1957	175.00	275.00	350.00

2913   *TOMMY*

SERIES: *Michael, Tommy, Mischief and Joan*

Modeller: Freda Doughty
Colourways: **A.** Pink shirt with gold highlights; turquoise shorts; yellow hair
  B. White shirt with pink and blue dots; blue shorts; brown hair
  C. Yellow shirt; purple shorts; yellow hair

Backstamp: **1.** Puce
  2. Black

R.W. No.	Backstamp	Height	Intro.	Discon.	Current Market Value U.K. £	U.S. $	Can. $
2913	Puce	4 1/2"	1931	1940	225.00	350.00	475.00
2913	B-2 to B-4	4 1/2"	1940	1957	175.00	275.00	350.00

2914   *MISCHIEF*

SERIES: *Michael, Tommy, Mischief and Joan*

Modeller: Freda Doughty
Colourways: **A.** Turquoise dress; lilac and yellow flowers on green and brown base
                 B. Yellow dress; pink flowers on green and brown base

Backstamp: **1.** Puce
                 2. Black

R.W. No.	Backstamp	Height	Intro.	Discon.	Current Market Value U.K. £	U.S. $	Can. $
2914	Puce	3 1/2"	1931	1940	250.00	375.00	500.00
2914	B-2 to B-4	3 1/2"	1940	1957	225.00	350.00	475.00

2915   *JOAN*

Modeller:	Freda Doughty
Colourways:	**A.** Orangey-red dress; yellow knickers
	B. White dress with blue dots; mauve knickers
	C. White dress, yellow bands with blue and red dotted pattern; pink knickers
	D. Yellow dress; purple knickers
Backstamp:	**1.** Puce
	2. Black

R.W. Stamp	Backstamp	Height	Intro.	Discon.	Current Market Value U.K. £	U.S. $	Can. $
2915	Puce	4 1/4"	1931	1940	225.00	350.00	475.00
2915	B-2 to B-4	4 1/4"	1940	1957	175.00	275.00	350.00

2924

THE FORTUNE TELLER
(MOTHER MACHREE)

Modeller: Freda Doughty
Colourways: **A.** Green dress; grey patterned shawl
B. Purple and orange dress; orangey-red shawl

Backstamp: **1.** Puce
2. Black

R.W. No.	Backstamp	Height	Intro.	Discon.	Current Market Value		
					U.K. £	U.S. $	Can. $
2924	Puce	5 3/4"	1931	1940	350.00	525.00	725.00
2924	B-2 to B-4	5 3/4"	1940	1957	275.00	425.00	575.00

2928   *MICHAEL POWDER BOWL*

Modeller:	Freda Doughty	
Colourways:	Boy wearing blue suit; grey bowl with blue, yellow and green design	
Backstamp:	**1.** Puce	
	2. Black	

R.W. No.	Backstamp	Height	Intro.	Discon.	Current Market Value		
					U.K. £	U.S. $	Can. $
2928	Puce	5 1/4"	1931	1940	275.00	375.00	500.00
2928	B-2 to B-4	5 1/4"	1940	1957	225.00	325.00	450.00

3008　　　　　　　　　　**SEA BREEZE**

Modeller: Freda Doughty
Colourways: **A.** Blue dress with green highlights; yellow hair; black and white seagull; brown, blue and green base
　　　　　　 B. Pink dress with yellow highlights; yellow hair; black and white seagull; brown, blue and green base

Backstamp: **1.** Puce
　　　　　　 2. Black

R.W. No.	Backstamp	Height	Intro.	Discon.	Current Market Value		
					U.K. £	U.S. $	Can. $
3008	Puce	8 1/2"	1932	1940	375.00	550.00	750.00
3008	B-2 to B-4	8 1/2"	1940	1959	300.00	425.00	600.00

3009

THE TREASURE
(BOY ON CUSHION)
(SLEEPING BOY)

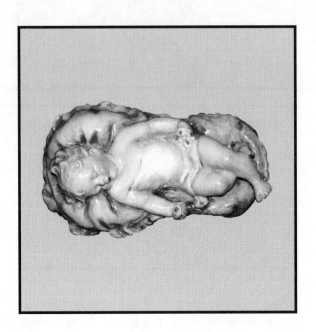

Modeller: Freda Doughty
Colour: Pale pink clothing; deep pink cushion; white daisies; green-brown base

Backstamp: 1. Puce
2. Black

R.W. No.	Backstamp	Length	Intro.	Discon.	Current Market Value		
					U.K. £	U.S. $	Can. $
3009	Puce	Unknown	1932	1940	450.00	650.00	875.00
3009	B-2		1940	1948	400.00	575.00	775.00

3010 *HAPPY BOY*

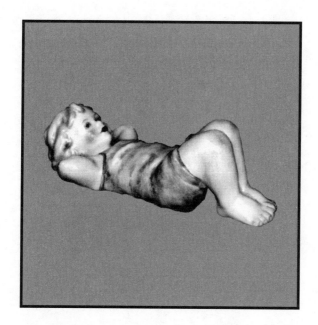

Modeller: Freda Doughty
Colour: Pink bathing suit with yellow trim; yellow hair

Backstamp: 1. Puce
2. Black

R.W. No.	Backstamp	Length	Intro.	Discon.	Current Market Value		
					U.K. £	U.S. $	Can. $
3010	Puce	5 1/2"	1932	1940	450.00	650.00	875.00
3010	B-2	5 1/2"	1940	1948	400.00	575.00	775.00

3012   **SPRING**

Modeller: Freda Doughty
Colourways: **A.** Lavender dress with dark mauve highlights; yellow hair; white lamb; purple flowers on green base
          B. Pink dress with yellow highlights; yellow hair; white lamb; pink flowers on green base

Backstamp: **1.** Puce
           2. Black

R.W. No.	Backstamp	Height	Intro.	Discon.	U.K. £	U.S. $	Can. $
					Current Market Value		
3012	Puce	8 1/2"	1932	1940	375.00	550.00	750.00
3012	B-2 to B-4	8 1/2"	1940	1959	300.00	450.00	600.00

3014   *MY FAVOURITE*

Modeller: Freda Doughty
Colourways: **A.** Blue dress with pink dots; yellow hair; white rabbits; green base
B. Blue dress with mauve highlights; yellow hair; brown and white rabbits; green base
C. Green dress; yellow hair; white rabbits; yellow flowers on base
D. Pink dress; yellow hair; white rabbits; pink flowers on green base

Backstamp: **1.** Puce
2. Black

R.W. No.	Backstamp	Height	Intro.	Discon.	Current Market Value U.K. £	U.S. $	Can. $
3014	Puce	5 1/2"	1932	1940	375.00	575.00	775.00
3014	B-2 to B-4	5 1/2"	1940	1959	300.00	450.00	625.00

3066   *EGYPT*

SERIES: *Children of the Nations*

Modeller: Freda Doughty
Colourways: Yellow robe with mauve and green stripes; red fez and shoes; brown base

Backstamp: 1. Puce
                2. Black

R.W. No.	Backstamp	Height	Intro.	Discon.	Current Market Value		
					U.K. £	U.S. $	Can. $
3066	Puce	5 3/4"	1934	1940	325.00	450.00	600.00
3066	B-2 to B-4	5 3/4"	1940	1959	275.00	400.00	500.00

3067A   *ITALY*

This model was also called "The Flower Girl" see page 16.

> ### SERIES: *Children of the Nations*

Modeller: Freda Doughty
Colourways: Green blouse; white fichu and apron; yellow and pink headscarf; pink and purple flowers

Backstamp: 1.   Puce
                          2.   Black

R.W. No.	Backstamp	Height	Intro.	Discon.	Current Market Value U.K. £	U.S. $	Can. $
3067A	Puce	3 3/4"	1934	1940	325.00	450.00	625.00
3067A	B-2 to B-4	3 3/4"	1940	1959	300.00	400.00	575.00

3067B   *THE FLOWER GIRL*

This model was also known as "Italy" see page 15.

Modeller: Freda Doughty
Colourways: Green blouse with purple decoration; mauve fichu and apron; yellow and purple headscarf; red, turquoise and purple flowers

Backstamp: 1. Puce
2. Black

R.W. No.	Backstamp	Height	Intro.	Discon.	Current Market Value		
					U.K. £	U.S. $	Can. $
3067B	Puce	3 3/4"	1934	1940	325.00	450.00	625.00
3067B	B-2 to B-4	3 3/4"	1940	1959	300.00	400.00	575.00

BURMAH

SERIES: *Children of the Nations*

Modeller: Freda Doughty
Colourways: Light blue loin cloth with dark blue highlights; red necklace and bracelets; brown and green base

Backstamp: 1. Puce
         2. Black

R.W. No.	Backstamp	Height	Intro.	Discon.	Current Market Value U.K. £	U.S. $	Can. $
3068	Puce	5 1/4"	1934	1940	150.00	250.00	300.00
3068	B-2 to B-4	5 1/4"	1940	1961	125.00	200.00	250.00
3068	B-5	5 1/4"	1962	1972	100.00	150.00	200.00

3069 GREECE

SERIES: *Children of the Nations*

Modeller: Freda Doughty
Colourways: Yellow blouse and stockings; black vest with orange and white trim; red sash; white skirt; red cap; brown base

Backstamp: 1. Puce
2. Black

R.W. No.	Backstamp	Height	Intro.	Discon.	Current Market Value		
					U.K. £	U.S. $	Can. $
3069	Puce	5 1/2"	1934	1940	325.00	500.00	675.00
3069	B-2 to B-4	5 1/2"	1940	1959	275.00	425.00	575.00

3070   *SPAIN*

SERIES: *Children of the Nations*

Modeller: Freda Doughty
Colourways: Pink dress; white apron with yellow and purple flowers; black sash; dark brown hair; yellow and mauve parasol

Backstamp: 1. Puce
           2. Black

R.W. No.	Backstamp	Height	Intro.	Discon.	U.K. £	U.S. $	Can. $
					Current Market Value		
3070	Puce	5 1/4"	1934	1940	350.00	500.00	675.00
3070	B-2 to B-4	5 1/4"	1940	1959	300.00	450.00	625.00

3071

INDIA

SERIES: *Children of the Nations*

Modeller: Freda Doughty
Colourways: **A.** White robe with purple highlights; blue turban; metal pipe
B. Yellow robe with purple highlights; blue turban; metal pipe

Backstamp: **1.** Puce
2. Black

R.W. No.	Backstamp	Height	Intro.	Discon.	Current Market Value		
					U.K. £	U.S. $	Can. $
3071	Puce	3 1/4"	1934	1940	150.00	250.00	300.00
3071	B-2 to B-4	3 1/4"	1940	1961	125.00	200.00	250.00
3071	B-5	3 1/4"	1962	1972	100.00	150.00	200.00

3072   *JAPAN*

SERIES: *Children of the Nations*

Modeller: Freda Doughty
Colourways: Flowered pink kimono; light green obi; dark brown hair; yellow fan

Backstamp: **1.** Puce
             2. Black

R.W. No.	Backstamp	Height	Intro.	Discon.	Current Market Value U.K. £	U.S. $	Can. $
3072	Puce	3 1/2"	1934	1940	500.00	750.00	950.00
3072	B-2 to B-4	3 1/2"	1940	1959	400.00	625.00	850.00

3073   *CHINA*

SERIES: *Children of the Nations*

Modeller: Freda Doughty
Colourways: A. Light green shirt with blue-green highlights on sleeves, collar, cuffs and coat edging; lavender trousers, maroon shoes; beige bowl
B. Yellow shirt; blue trousers; purple shoes; turquoise bowl

Backstamp: 1. Puce
2. Black

R.W. No.	Backstamp	Height	Intro.	Discon.	Current Market Value U.K. £	U.S. $	Can. $
3073	Puce	2 1/4"	1934	1940	150.00	250.00	300.00
3073	B-2 to B-4	2 1/4"	1940	1961	125.00	200.00	250.00
3073	B-5	2 1/4"	1962	1972	100.00	150.00	200.00

3074 HOLLAND

SERIES: *Children of the Nations*

Modeller: Freda Doughty
Colourways: Blue blouse; white skirt with blue checks; pink and white scarf; white hat; fawn clogs

Backstamp: 1. Puce
2. Black

R.W. No.	Backstamp	Height	Intro.	Discon.	Current Market Value		
					U.K. £	U.S. $	Can. $
3074	Puce	5 1/2"	1934	1940	350.00	525.00	725.00
3074	B-2 to B-4	5 1/2"	1940	1959	325.00	475.00	650.00

3075   *ENGLAND*

SERIES: *Children of the Nations*

Modeller: Freda Doughty
Colourways: **A.** Blue dress; yellow hair; white flowers; white flowers on green and yellow base
              B. Pink dress; yellow hair; white flowers; white flowers on green and yellow base

Backstamp: **1.** Puce
              2. Black

R.W. No.	Backstamp	Height	Intro.	Discon.	Current Market Value		
					U.K. £	U.S. $	Can. $
3075	Puce	5 1/4"	1934	1940	325.00	500.00	675.00
3075	B-2 to B-4	5 1/4"	1940	1959	300.00	450.00	625.00

3076   *WOODLAND DANCE*

Modeller: Freda Doughty
Colourways: **A.** Blue dress; brown hair; light brown rabbits; red-brown squirrel; green base
  B. Pink dress; yellow hair; light brown rabbits; brown squirrel; green base
  C. Yellow dress; yellow hair; brown rabbits; red squirrel; green base

Backstamp: **1.** Puce
  2. Black

R.W. No.	Backstamp	Height	Intro.	Discon.	Current Market Value		
					U.K. £	U.S. $	Can. $
3076	Puce	4"	1934	1940	250.00	375.00	500.00
3076	B-2 to B-4	4"	1940	1961	225.00	325.00	425.00
3076	B-5	4"	1962	1972	200.00	300.00	400.00

3081A   GRANDMOTHER'S DRESS

VERSION ONE: *Right Hand Flat to Dress*

Modeller: Freda Doughty

Colourways:
- **A.** Blue dress with white frills; white mob cap with blue ribbon; gloss finish
- **B.** Blue dress with white frills; blue mob cap; gold highlights; matte finish
- **C.** Creamy-yellow dress with blue frills and hem; white mob cap with blue frill; gloss finish
- **D.** Creamy-yellow dress with pink frills and hem; white mob cap with pink frill; gloss finish
- **E.** Green dress with white frills, white mob cap with green ribbon; gloss finish
- **F.** Green dress with white frills; green mob cap; gold highlights; matte finish
- **G.** Pink dress with white frills, white mob cap with pink ribbon; gloss finish
- **H.** Pink dress with white frills; pink mob cap; gold highlights; matte finish
- **I.** Red dress with white frills, red mob cap; gloss finish
- **J.** Red dress with white frills, red mob cap; gold highlights; matte finish
- **K.** Yellow dress with white frills, white mob cap with yellow ribbon; gloss finish
- **L.** Yellow dress with white frills; yellow mob cap; gold highlights; matte finish

Backstamp:
1. Puce
2. Black

R.W. No.	Backstamp	Height	Intro.	Discon.	Current Market Value		
					U.K. £	U.S. $	Can. $
3081A	Puce	6 1/4"	1935	1940	125.00	225.00	300.00
3081A	B-2 to B-4	6 1/4"	1940	1961	110.00	200.00	250.00
3081A	B-5	6 1/4"	1962	1980	80.00	150.00	200.00

3081B   *GRANDMOTHER'S DRESS*

VERSION TWO: *Right Hand Raised on Dress*

Modeller: Freda Doughty
Colourways: Yellow dress with white frills; white mob cap with yellow ribbon; gloss
Backstamp: 1.   Puce
               2.   Black

R.W. No.	Backstamp	Height	Intro.	Discon.	Current Market Value U.K. £	U.S. $	Can. $
3081B	Puce	6 3/4"	1935	1940	125.00	225.00	300.00
3081B	B-2 to B-4	6 3/4"	1940	1961	110.00	200.00	250.00
3081B	B-5	6 3/4"	1962	1980	80.00	150.00	200.00

Miniature

LITTLE GRANDMOTHER'S DRESS

All miniatures were issued without Royal Worcester models numbers.

Colourways: Green dress; yellow hair
Backstamp: Black

R.W. No.	Backstamp	Height	Intro.	Discon.	Current Market Value U.K. £	U.S. $	Can. $
—	B-5	3"	1982	By 1985	125.00	195.00	250.00

3082   *THE FIRST CUCKOO*

Modeller: Freda Doughty
Colourways: Pink dress; white petticoat; yellow hair; yellow flowers

Backstamp: 1. Puce
              2. Black

R.W. No.	Backstamp	Height	Intro.	Discon.	Current Market Value U.K. £	U.S. $	Can. $
3082	Puce	6 1/2"	1935	1940	375.00	550.00	725.00
3082	B-2 to B-4	6 1/2"	1940	1959	300.00	450.00	600.00

SUNSHINE

Modeller: Freda Doughty

Colourways: A. Pink dress; yellow hair; lilac flowers
B. White dress; yellow hair; lilac flowers

Backstamp: 1. Puce
2. Black

R.W. No.	Backstamp	Height	Intro.	Discon.	Current Market Value		
					U.K. £	U.S. $	Can. $
3083	Puce	5"	1935	1940	500.00	775.00	950.00
3083	B-2 to B-4	5"	1940	1959	400.00	625.00	850.00

THE DANDELION

Modeller: Freda Doughty
Colourways: Blue suit; yellow hair; white rabbits; green base

Backstamp: **1.** Puce
　　　　　 2. Black

R.W. No.	Backstamp	Height	Intro.	Discon.	Current Market Value		
					U.K. £	U.S. $	Can. $
3084	Puce	4"	1935	1940	500.00	775.00	950.00
3084	B-2 to B-4	4"	1940	1959	400.00	625.00	850.00

3087

BOY WITH PARAKEET
(PARAKEET)

Modeller:	Freda Doughty
Colourways:	**A.** Blue suit with white frills; lavender bird; gloss finish
	B. Blue suit with white frills; gold highlights; lavender bird; matte finish
	C. Pink suit with white frills; purple bird; gloss finish
	D. Pink suit with white frills; gold highlights; purple bird; matte finish
	E. Red suit with white frills; grey bird; gloss finish
	F. Red suit with white frills; gold highlights; grey bird; matte finish
	G. Yellow suit with white frills; green bird; gloss finish
	H. Yellow suit with white frills; gold highlights; green bird; matte finish
Backstamp:	**1.** Puce
	2. Black

R.W. No.	Backstamp	Height	Intro.	Discon.	Current Market Value U.K. £	U.S. $	Can. $
3087	Puce	6 3/4"	1935	1940	175.00	250.00	325.00
3087	B-2 to B-4	6 3/4"	1940	1961	110.00	200.00	250.00
3087	B-5	6 3/4"	1962	1980	80.00	175.00	225.00

Miniature

LITTLE PARAKEET BOY

Colourways:	Green suit; yellow hair
Backstamp:	Black

R.W. No.	Backstamp	Height	Intro.	Discon.	Current Market Value U.K. £	U.S. $	Can. $
—	B-5	3"	1982	By 1985	125.00	195.00	250.00

3103

WALES

SERIES: *Children of the Nations*

Modeller:	Freda Doughty
Colourways:	Pink dress; white apron; black hat; yellow flowers; green and yellow base
Backstamp:	1. Puce
	2. Black

R.W. No.	Backstamp	Height	Intro.	Discon.	Current Market Value		
					U.K. £	U.S. $	Can. $
3103	Puce	5 1/2"	1935	1940	325.00	475.00	650.00
3103	B-2 to B-4	5 1/2"	1940	1959	300.00	425.00	600.00

SERIES: *Children of the Nations*

Modeller: Freda Doughty
Colourways: Deep rose jacket; green and yellow kilt; brown and beige sporran; yellow hair; purple and green base

Backstamp: 1. Puce
          2. Black

R.W. No.	Backstamp	Height	Intro.	Discon.	Current Market Value		
					U.K. £	U.S. $	Can. $
3104	Puce	5 1/2"	1935	1940	325.00	475.00	650.00
3104	B-2 to B-4	5 1/2"	1940	1959	275.00	425.00	575.00

3106A

THE DUCHESS'S DRESS

STYLE ONE: **Hand Beneath Rose**

Modeller: Freda Doughty
Colourways: Turquoise dress with lavender highlights; brown hair; red rose

Backstamp: 1. Puce
2. Black

R.W. No.	Backstamp	Height	Intro.	Discon.	Current Market Value		
					U.K. £	U.S. $	Can. $
3106A	Puce	9 1/2"	1935	1940	400.00	625.00	850.00
3106A	B-2 to B-4	9 1/2"	1940	1959	300.00	450.00	625.00

3106B   *THE DUCHESS'S DRESS*

STYLE TWO: *Hand to the Side of Rose*

Modeller: Freda Doughty
Colourways: Turquoise dress with mauve highlights; brown hair; red roses

Backstamp: **1.**   Puce
             2.   Black

R.W. No.	Backstamp	Height	Intro.	Discon.	Current Market Value U.K. £	U.S. $	Can. $
3106B	Puce	6 1/2"	1935	1940	275.00	425.00	575.00
3106B	B-2 to B-4	6 1/2"	1940	1959	225.00	350.00	475.00

SISTER

Modeller: Freda Doughty

Colourways: **A.** Sister — pink dress
Brother — green jacket; white trousers
B. Sister —yellow dress with red flower design
Brother — blue jacket and trousers

Backstamp: **1.** Puce
2. Black

R.W. No.	Backstamp	Height	Intro.	Discon.	Current Market Value		
					U.K. £	U.S. $	Can. $
3149	Puce	6 3/4"	1936	1940	450.00	700.00	950.00
3149	B-2 to B-4	6 3/4"	1940	1959	350.00	525.00	725.00

3150   **TWO BABIES**

Modeller: Freda Doughty
Colourways: **A.** Blue vest; yellow shorts; white and brown puppy; yellow flowers on green and brown base
           B. White vest with blue trim; white and brown puppy; yellow flowers on green and brown base

Backstamp: **1.** Puce
            2. Black

R.W. No.	Backstamp	Height	Intro.	Discon.	Current Market Value		
					U.K. £	U.S. $	Can. $
3150	Puce	3 3/4"	1936	1940	375.00	575.00	775.00
3150	B-2 to B-4	3 3/4"	1940	1956	275.00	425.00	575.00

3151   *WATER BABY*

Modeller: Freda Doughty
Colourways: Flesh colouring; yellow hair; brown rock; blue and turquoise base

Backstamp: **1.** Puce
　　　　　　2. Black

R.W. No.	Backstamp	Height	Intro.	Discon.	Current Market Value U.K. £	U.S. $	Can. $
3151	Puce	6 1/4"	1936	1940	375.00	575.00	775.00
3151	B-2 to B-4	6 1/4"	1940	1959	325.00	475.00	675.00

3160 BUBBLES

Modeller: Freda Doughty
Colourways: **A.** Pale blue dress; white bowl with blue band; white circular base with blue band
B. Pink dress; white bowl with pink band; white circular base with pink band
C. Pink dress; white bowl with pink band; white circular base with pink, yellow and white patterned band

Backstamp: **1.** Puce
2. Black

R.W. No.	Backstamp	Height	Intro.	Discon.	Current Market Value		
					U.K. £	U.S. $	Can. $
3160	Puce	6 1/2"	1936	1940	600.00	925.00	1,250.00
3160	B-2 to B-4	6 1/2"	1940	1959	500.00	775.00	950.00

SERIES: *Children of the Nations*

Modeller: Freda Doughty
Colourways: A. Green dress; green scarf; white apron; brown hair; light brown basket
　　　　　　　B. Green and white striped dress; pink scarf; white apron; brown hair; brown basket

Backstamp: 1. Puce
　　　　　　　2. Black

R.W. No.	Backstamp	Height	Intro.	Discon.	Current Market Value U.K. £	U.S. $	Can. $
3178	Puce	5 3/4"	1936	1940	325.00	475.00	625.00
3178	B-2 to B-4	5 3/4"	1940	1959	275.00	375.00	525.00

3224

THE BRIDESMAID
(ROSE MAIDEN)

Modeller: Freda Doughty
Colourways: **A.** Blue dress with white highlights; yellow shoe; pink flowers; brown hair; blue head band
B. White dress; green shoe; pink flowers; brown hair; green head band

Backstamp: **1.** Puce
2. Black

R.W. No.	Backstamp	Height	Intro.	Discon.	Current Market Value U.K. £	U.S. $	Can. $
3224	Puce	8 1/4"	1938	1940	550.00	850.00	1,100.00
3224	B-2 to B-4	8 1/4	1940	1955	450.00	700.00	950.00

3225   *DANCING WAVES*

Modeller: Freda Doughty
Colourways: **A.** Pink dress; blue, yellow and white base
B. Turquoise dress; blue and white base

Backstamp: **1.** Puce
2. Black

R.W. No.	Backstamp	Height	Intro.	Discon.	Current Market Value U.K. £	U.S. $	Can. $
3225	Puce	8 3/4"	1938	1940	500.00	750.00	950.00
3225	B-2 to B-4	8 3/4"	1940	1959	400.00	625.00	850.00

3226 **ONLY ME**

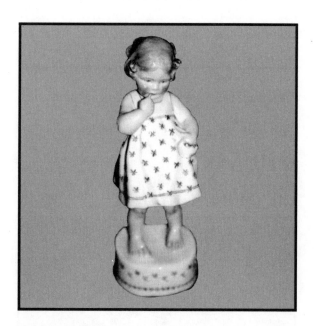

Modeller: Freda Doughty
Colourways: **A.** Pink and rose dress; lilac base
B. Pink dress with deep pink star design; brown hair; pink base with star design
C. White dress with pink bodice and pink dots on skirt; white base

Backstamp: **1.** Puce
2. Black

R.W. No.	Backstamp	Height	Intro.	Discon.	Current Market Value U.K. £	U.S. $	Can. $
3226	Puce	5 1/2"	1938	1940	225.00	350.00	475.00
3226	B-2 to B-4	5 1/2"	1940	1961	150.00	250.00	325.00
3226	B-5	5 1/2"	1962	1972	125.00	225.00	300.00

Miniature

SOLITAIRE

Colourways: Yellow dress with an orange border; dark brown hair; yellow base
Backstamp: Black

R.W. No.	Backstamp	Height	Intro.	Discon.	Current Market Value U.K. £	U.S. $	Can. $
—	B-5	3"	1982	By 1985	300.00	450.00	625.00

3256 BUT THE CHILD THAT IS BORN ON THE SABBATH DAY
(SUNDAY'S CHILD — BOY)

SERIES: *Days of the Week*

Modeller: Freda Doughty
Colourways: Blue outfit; green ball with red and blue stripes; yellow sandy base

Backstamp: 1. Puce
2. Black

R.W. No.	Backstamp	Height	Intro.	Discon.	Current Market Value U.K. £	U.S. $	Can. $
3256	Puce	4 1/4"	1938	1940	200.00	300.00	400.00
3256	B-2 to B-4	4 1/4"	1940	1961	125.00	200.00	275.00
3256	B-5	4 1/4"	1962	1985	100.00	175.00	250.00

Miniature

SUNSHINE DAYS

Colourways: Blue outfit; green ball with red and blue stripes; yellow sandy base
Backstamp: Black

R.W. No.	Backstamp	Height	Intro.	Discon.	Current Market Value U.K. £	U.S. $	Can. $
—	B-5	3"	1982	By 1985	125.00	195.00	250.00

3257

MONDAY'S CHILD IS FAIR OF FACE
(MONDAY'S CHILD — GIRL)   (SUSIE)

SERIES: *Days of the Week*

Modeller: Freda Doughty
Colourways: **A.** Blue dress trimmed with yellow frills and sash; white base with blue and yellow design
B. Creamy-white dress trimmed with blue frills and sash; light blue base

Backstamp: **1.** Puce
2. Black

R.W. No.	Backstamp	Height	Intro.	Discon.	Current Market Value U.K. £	U.S. $	Can. $
3257	Puce	6 1/2"	1938	1940	200.00	300.00	400.00
3257	B-2 to B-4	6 1/2"	1940	1961	125.00	225.00	275.00
3257	B-5	6 1/2"	1962	1985	100.00	175.00	250.00

Miniature

BIRTHDAY GIRL

Colourways: Blue dress; yellow hair
Backstamp: Black

R.W. No.	Backstamp	Height	Intro.	Discon.	Current Market Value U.K. £	U.S. $	Can. $
—	B-5	3"	1982	By 1985	125.00	195.00	250.00

3258A

TUESDAY'S CHILD IS FULL OF GRACE
(TUESDAY'S CHILD — GIRL)

First discontinued in 1985, model 3258A was re-introduced in 1994. This model was also called "Red Shoes" see page 47.

SERIES: *Days of the Week*

Modeller: Freda Doughty
Colourways: Yellow and white tutu trimmed with orange; yellow and red slippers

Backstamp: 1. Puce
2. Black

R.W. No.	Backstamp	Height	Intro.	Discon.	Current Market Value U.K. £	U.S. $	Can. $
3258A	Puce	8 1/2"	1938	1940	225.00	350.00	475.00
3258A	B-2 to B-4	8 1/2"	1940	1961	150.00	250.00	300.00
3258A	B-5	8 1/2"	1962	1985	125.00	200.00	275.00
3258A	B-6	8 1/2"	1994	Current	85.00	150.00	200.00

Miniature

BALLERINA

Colourways: Pink tutu; yellow hair
Backstamp: Black

R.W. No.	Backstamp	Height	Intro.	Discon.	Current Market Value U.K. £	U.S. $	Can. $
—	Black	3"	1982	By 1985	125.00	235.00	325.00

3258B   *RED SHOES*

This model was also called "Tuesday's Child is Full of Grace" or "Tuesday's Child — Girl" see page 46.

Modeller: Freda Doughty
Colourways: White tutu; red slippers
Backstamp: 1. Puce
2. Black

R.W. No.	Backstamp	Height	Intro.	Discon.	Current Market Value U.K. £	U.S. $	Can. $
3258B	Puce	8 1/2"	1938	1940	225.00	350.00	475.00
3258B	B-2 to B-4	8 1/2"	1940	1961	150.00	250.00	300.00
3258B	B-5	8 1/2"	1962	1982	125.00	200.00	250.00

3259

WEDNESDAY'S CHILD IS FULL OF WOE
(WEDNESDAY'S CHILD — GIRL)

SERIES: *Days of the Week*

Modeller: Freda Doughty
Colourways: Rose-pink dress; blue shoes; red hair; green and white base
Backstamp: **1.** Puce
2. Black

R.W. No.	Backstamp	Height	Intro.	Discon.	Current Market Value		
					U.K. £	U.S. $	Can. $
3259	Puce	7"	1938	1940	175.00	275.00	350.00
3259	B-2 to B-4	7"	1940	1961	150.00	250.00	300.00
3259	B-5	7"	1962	1985	125.00	200.00	250.00

Miniature

LOST SLIPPER

Colourways: Blue dress; brown hair
Backstamp: Black

R.W. No.	Backstamp	Height	Intro.	Discon.	Current Market Value		
					U.K. £	U.S. $	Can. $
—	B-5	3"	1982	By 1985	125.00	195.00	250.00

3260A   *THURSDAY'S CHILD HAS FAR TO GO*
(THURSDAY'S CHILD — BOY)

This model was also called "Smiling Through," see page 50.

     SERIES: Days of the Week

Modeller: Freda Doughty   **Backstamp:**   **1.**   Blue
Colourways: Light blue coat; red hat, sandals;   **2.**   Black
             multi-coloured scarf; dark brown staff

R.W. No.	Backstamp	Height	Intro.	Discon.	Current Market Value U.K. £	U.S. $	Can. $
3260A	Puce	6 1/2"	1938	1940	200.00	300.00	400.00
3260A	B-2 to B-4	6 1/2"	1940	1961	150.00	250.00	300.00
3260A	B-5	6 1/2"	1962	1985	125.00	200.00	250.00

Miniature

COUNTRY BOY

Colourways: Blue coat; yellowhair
Backstamp: Black

R.W. No.	Backstamp	Height	Intro.	Discon.	Current Market Value U.K. £	U.S. $	Can. $
—	B-5	3"	1982	By 1985	125.00	195.00	250.00

3260B   *SMILING THROUGH*

This model was also called "Thursday's Child Has Far To Go" or "Thursday's Boy," see page 49.

Modeller: Freda Doughty
Colourways: Light blue coat; brown hat and sandals; dark brown staff

Backstamp: 1. Blue, puce script
          2. Black

R.W. No.	Backstamp	Height	Intro.	Discon.	Current Market Value U.K. £	U.S. $	Can. $
3260B	Puce	6 1/2"	1938	1940	200.00	300.00	400.00
3260B	B-2 to B-4	6 1/2"	1940	1961	150.00	250.00	300.00
3260B	B-5	6 1/2"	1962	1982	125.00	200.00	250.00

3261A   *FRIDAY'S CHILD IS LOVING AND GIVING*
(FRIDAY'S CHILD — BOY)

This model was also called "My Pet," see page 52.

SERIES: *Days of the Week*

Modeller:	Freda Doughty			**Backstamp:**	**1.**	Puce
Colourways:	Beige and white top; green shorts; orange sandals; grey kitten; green and white base				**2.**	Black

R.W. No.	Backstamp	Height	Intro.	Discon.	**Current Market Value** U.K. £	U.S. $	Can. $
3261A	Puce	7"	1938	1940	200.00	300.00	400.00
3261A	B-2 to B-4	7"	1940	1961	150.00	250.00	300.00
3261A	B-5	7"	1962	1985	125.00	200.00	250.00

Miniature

OLD FRIENDS

Colourways: Blue top; dark blue shorts; yellow hair
Backstamp: Black

R.W. No.	Backstamp	Height	Intro.	Discon.	**Current Market Value** U.K. £	U.S. $	Can. $
—	B-6	3"	1982	By 1985	125.00	195.00	250.00

3261B   *MY PET*

This model was also called "Friday's Child is Loving and Giving" or "Friday's Child — Boy," see page 51.

Modeller: Freda Doughty
Colourways: Blue top and shorts; brown hair; grey cat

Backstamp: 1. Puce
                    2. Black

R.W. No.	Backstamp	Height	Intro.	Discon.	Current Market Value U.K. £	U.S. $	Can. $
3261B	Puce	7"	1938	1940	200.00	300.00	400.00
3261B	B-2 to B-4	7"	1940	1961	150.00	250.00	300.00
3261B	B-5	7"	1962	1982	125.00	200.00	275.00

3262   *SATURDAY'S CHILD WORKS HARD FOR A LIVING*
(SATURDAY'S CHILD — GIRL)

SERIES: *Days of the Week*

Modeller: Freda Doughty
Colourways: **A.** Blue dress; yellow wool; black and white kitten
                B. White dress trimmed with dark blue; red wool; black and white kitten; lavender base

Backstamp: **1.** Blue
              2. Black

R.W. No.	Backstamp	Height	Intro.	Discon.	Current Market Value U.K. £	U.S. $	Can. $
3262	Blue	5 3/4"	1938	1940	200.00	300.00	400.00
3262	B-2 to B-4	5 3/4"	1940	1961	150.00	250.00	300.00
3262	B-5	5 3/4"	1962	1985	125.00	200.00	250.00

Miniature

KATIE

Colourways: Blue dress; yellow hair
Backstamp: Black

R.W. No.	Backstamp	Height	Intro.	Discon.	Current Market Value U.K. £	U.S. $	Can. $
—	B-6	3"	1982	By 1985	125.00	195.00	250.00

Modeller: Freda Doughty

Colourways: **A.** Burgundy dress with white highlights; white and brown dog; green and brown base

B. Pale blue dress with lavender highlights; white and brown dog; green and brown base

Backstamp: **1.** Puce

2. Black

R.W. No.	Backstamp	Height	Intro.	Discon.	Current Market Value U.K. £	U.S. $	Can. $
3270	Puce	6 3/4"	1938	1940	425.00	650.00	875.00
3270	B-2 to B-4	6 3/4"	1940	1959	375.00	550.00	725.00

3301   *LITTLE MISS MUFFET*

SERIES: *Nursery Rhymes*

Modeller: Freda Doughty
Colourways: Rose-pink outer dress; yellow sleeves; white under dress with pink and green pattern; blue bowl; green tuffet; brown and black spider

Backstamp: 1. Puce
2. Black

R.W. No.	Backstamp	Height	Intro.	Discon.	· Current Market Value		
					U.K. £	U.S. $	Can. $
3301	Puce	4 1/2"	1940	1940	400.00	625.00	850.00
3301	B-2 to B-4	4 1/2"	1940	1959	300.00	450.00	625.00

_3302_   **_BABES IN THE WOOD_**

SERIES: _Nursery Rhymes_

Modeller: Freda Doughty
Colourways: Boy — pink pinafore; purple blouse and shoes
               Girl — blue dress; purple cap trimmed with white

Backstamp: 1. Puce
               2. Black

R.W. No.	Backstamp	Height	Intro.	Discon.	Current Market Value		
					U.K. £	U.S. $	Can. $
3302	Puce	6 1/4"	1940	1940	500.00	750.00	950.00
3302	B-2 to B-4	6 1/4"	1940	1959	400.00	600.00	825.00

3303   *POLLY PUT THE KETTLE ON*

SERIES: *Nursery Rhymes*

Modeller: Freda Doughty
Colourways: **A.** White dress; pink apron; white cap trimmed with pink; brown shoes; gold kettle
B. White dress; pink apron; white cap trimmed with pink; brown shoes; silver kettle

Backstamp: **1.** Puce
2. Black

R.W. No.	Backstamp	Height	Intro.	Discon.	Current Market Value U.K. £	U.S. $	Can. $
3303	Puce	6"	1940	1940	250.00	375.00	500.00
3303	B-2 to B-4	6"	1940	1961	150.00	250.00	300.00
3303	B-5	6"	1962	1975	125.00	200.00	250.00

Miniature

MOTHER'S HELPER

Colourways: Unknown
Backstamp: Black

R.W. No.	Backstamp	Height	Intro.	Discon.	Current Market Value U.K. £	U.S. $	Can. $
—	Black	3"	1982	By 1985	125.00	195.00	250.00

3304   *GOOSEY GOOSEY GANDER*

SERIES: *Nursery Rhymes*

Modeller: Freda Doughty
Colourways: Yellow smock with white collar; green shorts; white and grey goose; orange beak, feet; green and beige base
Backstamp: 1. Puce
              2. Black

R.W. No.	Backstamp	Height	Intro.	Discon.	Current Market Value		
					U.K. £	U.S. $	Can. $
3304	Puce	6"	1940	1940	400.00	625.00	850.00
3304	B-2 to B-4	6"	1940	1959	300.00	450.00	625.00

3305   *LITTLE JACK HORNER*

SERIES: *Nursery Rhymes*

Modeller: Freda Doughty
Colourways: Green and beige tunic; white blouse; yellow breeches; green stockings; beige shoes; yellow hair

Backstamp: 1. Puce
            2. Black

R.W. No.	Backstamp	Height	Intro.	Discon.	Current Market Value		
					U.K. £	U.S. $	Can. $
3305	Puce	4 1/4"	1940	1940	375.00	575.00	775.00
3305	B-2 to B-4	4 1/4"	1940	1959	300.00	450.00	625.00

3306   *LITTLE BOY BLUE*

SERIES: *Nursery Rhymes*

Modeller: Freda Doughty
Colourways: Blue suit with white collar, blue hat and shoes; yellow horn; white sheep with lavender and beige highlights; beige base

Backstamp: 1. Puce
2. Black

R.W. No.	Backstamp	Height	Intro.	Discon.	Current Market Value		
					U.K. £	U.S. $	Can. $
3306	Puce	3 1/2"	1940	1940	400.00	625.00	850.00
3306	B-2 to B-4	3 1/2"	1940	1959	300.00	450.00	625.00

3359

THE BOW
(MASQUERADE BOY)

Modeller: Freda Doughty
Colourways: **A.** Creamy-white suit with white and grey collar and cuffs; burgundy sash; brown hair; green and cream base
B. Turquoise suit with white collar and cuffs; burgundy sash; yellow hair; brown shoes; cream base

Backstamp: Black

R.W. No.	Backstamp	Height	Intro.	Discon.	Current Market Value		
					U.K. £	U.S. $	Can. $
3359	B-2 to B-4	6 3/4"	1941	1962	225.00	350.00	475.00
3359	B-5	6 3/4"	1962	1974	150.00	225.00	300.00

3360

THE CURTSEY
(MASQUERADE GIRL)

Modeller: Freda Doughty
Colourways: **A.** Cream dress edged with blue dots; cream bows; silver shoes; yellow hair
B. Pink dress; white bodice and skirt with pink and green pattern; green bows and shoes; brown hair

Backstamp: Black

R.W. No.	Backstamp	Height	Intro.	Discon.	Current Market Value		
					U.K. £	**U.S. $**	**Can. $**
3360	B-2 to B-4	5 3/4"	1941	1962	275.00	400.00	550.00
3360	B-5	5 3/4"	1962	1974	200.00	300.00	400.00

380   *SEATED CHILD*

Modeller: Freda Doughty
Colourways: Flesh colouring; yellow hair

Backstamp: Black

R.W. No.	Backstamp	Height	Intro.	Discon.	Current Market Value		
					U.K. £	U.S. $	Can. $
380	B-2 to B-4	4"	1942	1955	500.00	750.00	950.00

3381 CRAWLING CHILD

Modeller: Freda Doughty
Colourways: Flesh colouring; yellow hair
Backstamp: Black

R.W. No.	Backstamp	Height	Intro.	Discon.	Current Market Value		
					U.K. £	U.S. $	Can.
3381	B-2 to B-4	3 3/4"	1942	1955	500.00	750.00	950.00

Burmah (3068), China(3073), Wales (3103), Scotland (3104) England (3075), Ireland (3178)

Spain (3070), Japan (3072), Greece (3069), Italy (3067), Holland (3074), India (3071) Egypt (3066)

December (3458), February (3453), January (3452), November (3418)

Thursday's Girl (3522), Sunday's Girl (3518), Thursday's Boy (3260), Tuesday's Boy (3534)

Little Miss Muffet (3301), Little Boy Blue (3306), Little Jack Horner (3305), Goosey Goosey Gander (3304)

Joan (2915), Michael (2912), Mischief (2914), Tommy (2913)

Various Colourways of Boy with Parakeet (3087)

Various Colourways of Grandmother's Dress (3081)

3416   *APRIL*

SERIES: *Months of the Year*

Modeller: Freda Doughty
Colourways: Yellow bodice, white skirt with yellow and lavender stripes; white lamb with brown markings; green base with yellow and white flowers

Backstamp: Black

R.W. No.	Backstamp	Height	Intro.	Discon.	Current Market Value U.K. £	U.S.$	Can. $
3416	B-4	6"	c.1950	1961	200.00	300.00	400.00
3416	B-5	6"	1962	1985	150.00	225.00	300.0

Miniature

SPRINGTIME

Colourways: White bodice, green skirt
Backstamp: Black

R.W. No.	Backstamp	Height	Intro.	Discon.	Current Market Value U.K. £	U.S.$	Can. $
—	B-5	3"	1982	By-1985	125.00	195.00	250.00

3417

OCTOBER

SERIES: *Months of the Year*

Modeller:	Freda Doughty
Colourways:	Yellow sweater with blue bands; blue shorts; brown hair; brown squirrels; green base
Backstamp:	Black

R.W. No.	Backstamp	Height	Intro.	Discon.	Current Market Value U.K. £	U.S.$	Can. $
3417	B-4	7 1/2"	c.1950	1961	200.00	300.00	400.00
3417	B-5	7 1/2"	1962	1985	150.00	225.00	300.00

Miniature

WOODLAND WALK

Colourways:	Unknown
Backstamp:	Black

R.W. No.	Backstamp	Height	Intro.	Discon.	Current Market Value U.K. £	U.S.$	Can. $
—	Black	3"	1982	By 1985	125.00	195.00	250.00

3418   *NOVEMBER*

The model November shows a young girl feeding a dove on her right arm and three doves are at her feet. In 1963, this model was reissued as Fantails, shape number 3760, and has only two doves at the girls feet (see page 119).

SERIES: *Months of the Year*

Modeller: Freda Doughty
Colourways: Lavender coat with cream highlights; leggings; orange hat; four white doves
Backstamp: Black

R.W. No.	Backstamp	Height	Intro.	Discon.	Current Market Value U.K. £	U.S.$	Can. $
3418	B-4	7 1/2"	c.1950	1961	225.00	350.00	525.00
3418	B-5	7 1/2"	1962	1985	175.00	275.00	350.00

Miniature

PEACE

Colourways: Pink hat and coat
Backstamp: Black

R.W. No.	Backstamp	Height	Intro.	Discon.	Current Market Value U.K. £	U.S.$	Can. $
—	B-5	3"	1982	By 1985	125.00	195.00	250.00

3433A

JOHNNIE

Modeller: Freda Doughty
Colourways: White shirt; green shorts; brown hair; yellow ducklings; green base
Backstamp: Black

R.W. No.	Backstamp	Height	Intro.	Discon.	Current Market Value		
					U.K. £	**U.S.$**	**Can. $**
3433A	B-2	6 1/2"	1947	Unknown	250.00	375.00	525.00

3433B

FARMER'S BOY
(YOUNG FARMER)

Modeller: Freda Doughty
Colourways: White shirt; blue shorts; brown hair; white and yellow ducklings; green base

Backstamp: Black

R.W. No.	Backstamp	Height	Intro.	Discon.	Current Market Value U.K. £	U.S.$	Can. $
3433B	B-4	6 1/2"	Unknown	1955	225.00	350.00	475.00

3435   *HAPPY DAYS*

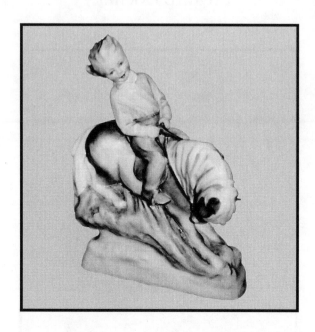

Modeller: Freda Doughty
Colourways: Light green shirt; blue-grey trousers; yellow hair; cream and brown pony; green grass; cream base
Backstamp: Black

R.W. No.	Backstamp	Height	Intro.	Discon.	Current Market Value U.K. £	U.S.$	Can. $
3435	B2 to B-3	7 1/2"	1948	1955	800.00	1,250.00	1,250.00

3440

JULY

SERIES: *Months of the Year*

Modeller:	Freda Doughty
Colourways:	Pink bathing suit; brown hair; blue and white base
Backstamp:	Black

R.W. No.	Backstamp	Height	Intro.	Discon.	Current Market Value U.K. £	U.S.$	Can. $
3440	B-4	7"	c.1950	1961	225.00	350.00	475.00
3440	B-5	7"	1962	1985	175.00	275.00	350.00

Miniature

AT THE SEASIDE

| **Colourways:** | Yellow bathing suit; brown hair |
| **Backstamp:** | Black |

R.W. No.	Backstamp	Height	Intro.	Discon.	Current Market Value U.K. £	U.S.$	Can. $
—	B-5	3"	1982	By 1985	125.00	195.00	250.00

3441 *AUGUST*

SERIES: *Months of the Year*

Modeller: Freda Doughty
Colourways: Flesh colouring; brown hair; blue base with white highlights; multi-coloured fish
Backstamp: Black

R.W. No.	Backstamp	Height	Intro.	Discon.	Current Market Value U.K. £	U.S.$	Can. $
3441	B-4	5"	c.1950	1961	175.00	275.00	350.00
3441	B-5	5"	1962	1985	150.00	250.00	300.00

Miniature

LITTLE MERMAID

Colourways: Flesh colouring; blue base
Backstamp: Black

R.W. No.	Backstamp	Height	Intro.	Discon.	Current Market Value U.K. £	U.S.$	Can. $
—	B-5	3"	1982	By 1985	125.00	195.00	250.00

SERIES: *Months of the Year*

Modeller: Freda Doughty
Colourways: Burgundy coat; beige leggings; brown shoes; green scarf; yellow hair
Backstamp: Black

R.W. No.	Backstamp	Height	Intro.	Discon.	Current Market Value U.K. £	U.S.$	Can. $
3452	B-4	6"	c.1950	1961	175.00	275.00	350.00
3452	B-5	6"	1962	1985	150.00	250.00	300.00

Miniature

THE SLIDE

Colourways: Light brown coat; dark brown shoes; blue scarf; yellow hair
Backstamp: Black

R.W. No.	Backstamp	Height	Intro.	Discon.	Current Market Value U.K. £	U.S.$	Can. $
—	B-5	3"	1982	1988	125.00	195.00	250.00

3453

FEBRUARY

SERIES: *Months of the Year*

Modeller: Freda Doughty
Colourways: **A.** Blue raincoat; black hat and wellingtons; brown and white base
B. Green raincoat; black hat and wellingtons; brown and white base
Backstamp: Black

R.W. No.	Backstamp	Height	Intro.	Discon.	Current Market Value U.K. £	U.S.$	Can. $
3453	B-4	6 1/4"	c.1950	1961	225.00	350.00	475.00
3453	B-5	6 1/4"	1962	1985	175.00	275.00	350.00

Miniature

FISHERMAN

Colourways: Yellow raincoat; green hat and wellingtons
Backstamp: Black

R.W. No.	Backstamp	Height	Intro.	Discon.	Current Market Value U.K. £	U.S.$	Can. $
—	Black	3"	1982	By 1985	125.00	195.00	250.00

3454   *MARCH*

SERIES: *Months of the Year*

Modeller: Freda Doughty
Colourways: Pink dress; blue hat; yellow hair; yellow shoes; green and beige base
Backstamp: Black

R.W. No.	Backstamp	Height	Intro.	Discon.	Current Market Value U.K. £	U.S.$	Can. $
3454	B-4	6"	c.1950	1961	225.00	350.00	475.00
3454	B-5	6"	1962	1985	175.00	275.00	350.00

Miniature

MARCH DAY

Colourways: White dress trimmed in green; green belt; brown hat; brown hair
Backstamp: Black

R.W. No.	Backstamp	Height	Intro.	Discon.	Current Market Value U.K. £	U.S.$	Can. $
—	B-5	3"	1982	By 1985	300.00	450.00	600.00

3455   *MAY*

SERIES: *Months of the Year*

Modeller: Freda Doughty
Colourways: Blue dress; yellow hair; white daisies on a green base
Backstamp: Black

R.W. No.	Backstamp	Height	Intro.	Discon.	Current Market Value U.K. £	U.S.$	Can. $
3455	B-4	5"	c.1950	1961	225.00	350.00	475.00
3455	B-5	5"	1962	1985	175.00	275.00	350.00

Miniature

DAISY CHAIN

Colourways: Pink dress; brown hair; yellow flowers and base
Backstamp: Black

R.W. No.	Backstamp	Height	Intro.	Discon.	Current Market Value U.K. £	U.S.$	Can. $
—	B-5	3"	1982	By 1985	275.00	375.00	500.00

3456 *JUNE*

SERIES: *Months of the Year*

Modeller: Freda Doughty
Colourways: White shirt; multi-coloured tie and belt; yellow shorts; yellow hair; brown dog; grey and green base
Backstamp: Black

R.W. No.	Backstamp	Height	Intro.	Discon.	Current Market Value U.K. £	U.S.$	Can. $
3456	B-4	6 1/2"	c.1950	1961	200.00	300.00	400.00
3456	B-5	6 1/2"	1962	1985	175.00	275.00	350.00

Miniature

MUSICAL MOMENTS

Colourways: Yellow shirt; blue shorts; yellow hair
Backstamp: Black

R.W. No.	Backstamp	Height	Intro.	Discon.	Current Market Value U.K. £	U.S.$	Can. $
—	B-5	3"	1982	By 1985	125.00	195.00	250.00

3457

SEPTEMBER
(SNOWY)

SERIES: *Months of the Year*

Modeller: Freda Doughty
Colourways: White shirt; blue tie, shorts, shoes and hat; white cat; green and beige base
Backstamp: Black

R.W. No.	Backstamp	Height	Intro.	Discon.	Current Market Value		
					U.K. £	U.S.$	Can. $
3457	B-4	4 1/2"	c.1950	1961	225.00	350.00	475.00
3457	B-5	4 1/2"	1962	1985	175.00	250.00	325.00

Miniature

CHRISTOPHER

Colourways: Yellow shirt; brown shorts; green shoes; yellow hat
Backstamp: Black

R.W. No.	Backstamp	Height	Intro.	Discon.	Current Market Value		
					U.K. £	U.S.$	Can. $
—	B-5	3"	1982	By 1985	125.00	195.00	250.00

SERIES: *Months of the Year*

Modeller: Freda Doughty
Colourways: Creamy-yellow coat and hat trimmed with burgundy; burgundy mittens and shoes
Backstamp: Black

R.W. No.	Backstamp	Height	Intro.	Discon.	Current Market Value U.K. £	U.S.$	Can. $
3458	B-4	6 1/2"	c.1950	1961	225.00	350.00	475.00
3458	B-5	6 1/2"	1962	1985	175.00	250.00	325.00

Miniature

SNOWBALL

Colourways: Red coat with white trim
Backstamp: Black

R.W. No.	Backstamp	Height	Intro.	Discon.	Current Market Value U.K. £	U.S.$	Can. $
—	B-5	3"	1982	By 1985	125.00	195.00	250.00

3471   BATTLEDORE

*Photograph not available
at press time*

Modeller: Freda Doughty
Colourways: Unknown
Backstamp: Black

R.W. No.	Backstamp	Height	Intro.	Discon.	Current Market Value U.K. £	U.S.$	Can. $
3471	B-4	Unknown	1951	1951	Not Issued		

3472 SHUTTLECOCK

Photograph not available
at press time

Modeller: Freda Doughty
Colourways: Unknown

Backstamp: Black

R.W. No.	Backstamp	Height	Intro.	Discon.	Current Market Value		
					U.K. £	U.S.$	Can. $
3472	B-4	Unknown	1951	1951	Not issued		

3479

PAUL

*Photograph not available
at press time*

Modeller: Freda Doughty
Colourways: Unknown
Backstamp: Black

R.W. No.	Backstamp	Height	Intro.	Discon.	Current Market Value U.K. £	U.S.$	Can. $
3479	B-4	Unknown	1952	1952		Rare	

3480　　　　　　　　　　*PRISCILLA*

Photograph not available
at press time

Modeller: Freda Doughty
Colourways: Unknown
Backstamp: Black

R.W. No.	Backstamp	Height	Intro.	Discon.	Current Market Value		
					U.K. £	U.S.$	Can. $
3480	B-4	Unknown	1952	1952		Rare	

3488 **PUNCH**

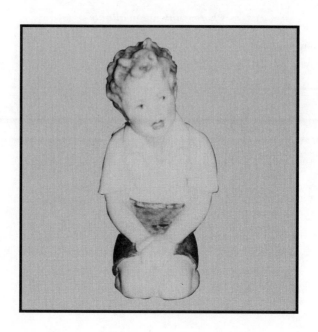

Modeller: Freda Doughty
Colourways: Yellow shirt with a white collar; pink belt; blue shorts; ginger hair
Backstamp: Black

R.W. No.	Backstamp	Height	Intro.	Discon.	Current Market Value		
					U.K. £	U.S.$	Can. $
3488	B-4	5 1/2"	1952	1959	500.00	775.00	950.00

3489   *JUDY*

Modeller: Freda Doughty
Colourways: Blue dress with white frills and purple highlights; yellow hair
Backstamp: Black

R.W. No.	Backstamp	Height	Intro.	Discon.	Current Market Value U.K. £	U.S.$	Can. $
3489	B-4	6"	1952	1959	500.00	775.00	950.00

3518   SUNDAY'S CHILD — GIRL

SERIES: *Days of the Week*

Modeller: Freda Doughty
Colourways: Dress has a blue bodice and a white skirt with red dots and hem; turquoise hat; blue shoes; yellow hair; green and white base

Backstamp: Black

R.W. No.	Backstamp	Height	Intro.	Discon.	Current Market Value U.K. £	U.S.$	Can. $
3518	B-4	7"	1954	1961	225.00	350.00	475.00
3518	B-5	7"	1962	1985	175.00	250.00	325.00

Miniature

LET'S RUN

Colourways: Red dress and shoes; white hat with red band; metal windmill
Backstamp: Black

R.W. No.	Backstamp	Height	Intro.	Discon.	Current Market Value U.K. £	U.S.$	Can. $
—	Black	3"	1982	By 1985	250.00	375.00	500.00

3519A MONDAY'S CHILD — BOY

This model was also named "All Mine," see page 88.

> **SERIES:** *Days of the Week*

Modeller: Freda Doughty
Colourways: Blue shirt, shorts and shoes; white and brown puppies
Backstamp: Black

R.W. No.	Backstamp	Height	Intro.	Discon.	Current Market Value		
					U.K. £	U.S.$	Can. $
3519A	B-4	7 1/4"	1954	1961	225.00	350.00	475.00
3519A	B-5	7 1/4"	1962	1985	175.00	250.00	325.00

Miniature

THREE'S COMPANY

Colourways: Brown shorts and hair
Backstamp: Black

R.W. No.	Backstamp	Height	Intro.	Discon.	Current Market Value		
					U.K. £	U.S.$	Can. $
—	B-5	3"	1982	By 1985	125.00	195.00	250.00

3519B   *ALL MINE*

This model was also named "Monday's Boy," see page 87.

Modeller: Freda Doughty
Colourways: Yellow shirt; green shorts; white shoes; white and brown puppies
Backstamp: Black

R.W. No.	Backstamp	Height	Intro.	Discon.	Current Market Value U.K. £	U.S.$	Can. $
3519B	B-4	7 1/4"	1954	1961	225.00	350.00	475.00
3519B	B-5	7 1/4"	1962	1982	175.00	250.00	325.00

SERIES: *Days of the Week*

Modeller: Freda Doughty
Colourways: Green top; orange shorts; red hair; grey teddy bear; orange and white base
Backstamp: Black

R.W. No.	Backstamp	Height	Intro.	Discon.	Current Market Value U.K. £	U.S.$	Can. $
3521	B-4	7"	1954	1961	225.00	350.00	475.00
3521	B-5	7"	1962	1985	175.00	250.00	325.00

Miniature

POOR TEDDY

Colourways: Yellow smock; brown hair
Backstamp: Black

R.W. No.	Backstamp	Height	Intro.	Discon.	Current Market Value U.K. £	U.S.$	Can. $
—	B-5	3"	1982	By 1985	125.00	195.00	250.00

3522   *THURSDAY'S CHILD — GIRL*

SERIES: *Days of the Week*

Modeller: Freda Doughty
Colourways: Turquoise dress with white collar and cuffs and a pink belt; rose-pink shoes; turquoise and pink hat; brown shoes; green beige and white base

Backstamp: Black

R.W. No.	Backstamp	Height	Intro.	Discon.	Current Market Value U.K. £	U.S.$	Can. $
3522	B-4	7 1/4"	1954	1961	200.00	300.00	400.00
3522	B-5	7 1/4"	1962	1985	150.00	250.00	300.00

Miniature

HOMETIME

Colourways: Blue coat and shoes
Backstamp: Black

R.W. No.	Backstamp	Height	Intro.	Discon.	Current Market Value U.K. £	U.S.$	Can. $
—	B-5	3"	1982	By 1985	125.00	195.00	250.00

3523   *FRIDAY'S CHILD — GIRL*

SERIES: *Days of the Week*

Modeller: Freda Doughty
Colourways: Yellow dungarees; brown bird; green base

Backstamp: Black

R.W. No.	Backstamp	Height	Intro.	Discon.	Current Market Value U.K. £	U.S.$	Can. $
3523	B-4	6"	1954	1961	225.00	350.00	475.00
3523	B-5	6"	1962	1985	175.00	250.00	325.00

Miniature

TEATIME

Colourways: Blue dress, yellow hair
Backstamp: Black

R.W. No.	Backstamp	Height	Intro.	Discon.	Current Market Value U.K. £	U.S.$	Can. $
—	B-5	3"	1982	By 1985	125.00	195.00	250.00

3524

SERIES: *Days of the Week*

Modeller: Freda Doughty
Colourways: White shirt and hat; blue overalls; brown and grey spade; brown and green base

Backstamp: Black

R.W. No.	Backstamp	Height	Intro.	Discon.	Current Market Value U.K. £	U.S.$	Can. $
3524	B-4	6 1/4"	1954	1961	200.00	300.00	400.00
3524	B-5	6 1/4"	1962	1985	150.00	250.00	300.00

Miniature

GARDENER

Colourways: Blue shirt; yellow hair
Backstamp: Black

R.W. No.	Backstamp	Height	Intro.	Discon.	Current Market Value U.K. £	U.S.$	Can. $
—	B-5	3"	1982	By 1985	125.00	195.00	250.00

SERIES: *Days of the Week*

Modeller: Freda Doughty
Colourways: Yellow sweater and hat with red stripes; blue trousers; brown skates; pale blue and white base
Backstamp: Black

R.W. No.	Backstamp	Height	Intro.	Discon.	Current Market Value U.K. £	U.S.$	Can. $
3534	B-4	6 1/4"	1954	1961	225.00	350.00	450.00
3534	B-5	6 1/4"	1962	1985	150.00	250.00	300.00

Miniature

THE SKATER

Colourways: Red coat
Backstamp: Black

R.W. No.	Backstamp	Height	Intro.	Discon.	Current Market Value U.K. £	U.S.$	Can. $
—	B-5	3"	1982	By 1985	125.00	195.00	250.00

3546A SPRING MORNING

First introduced as Spring Morning in 1955, (B-4), this model was reintroduced as Spring Morn (B-5), in 1982.

STYLE ONE: *6 Inches*

Modeller: Freda Doughty

Colourways: **A.** Green dress with white collar and cuffs; pink sash; dark green hat; yellow flowers in light brown basket

B. Green dress; white apron with yellow flowered design; yellow hat

C. Red dress with white collar and cuffs; turquoise sash; blue hat

Backstamp: Black

R.W. No.	Backstamp	Height	Intro.	Discon.	Current Market Value		
					U.K. £	U.S.$	Can. $
3546A	B-4	6"	1955	1962	250.00	375.00	500.00
3546A	B-5	6"	1982	c.1985	200.00	300.00	400.00

3546B   **SPRING MORNING**

STYLE TWO: *9 Inches*

Modeller: Freda Doughty
Colourways: Orange dress with white collar and cuffs; green sash; green hat; yellow flowers in light brown basket
Backstamp: Black

R.W. No.	Backstamp	Height	Intro.	Discon.	Current Market Value U.K. £	U.S.$	Can. $
3546B	B-4	9"	1955	1961	300.00	450.00	600.00
3546B	B-5	9"	1962	1962	225.00	350.00	450.00

3547A   SUMMER DAY

First discontinued in 1958, this model was reintroduced in 1982.

STYLE ONE: *7 1/2 Inches*

Modeller: Freda Doughty
Colourways: Dress with blue bodice and white flowered skirt; blue sash and underskirts
Backstamp: Black

R.W. No.	Backstamp	Height	Intro.	Discon.	Current Market Value		
					U.K. £	U.S.$	Can. $
3547A	B-4	7 1/2"	1955	1958	375.00	575.00	775.00
3547A	B-5	7 1/2"	1982	c.1985	325.00	475.00	600.00

3547B   *SUMMER DAY*

STYLE TWO: *9 1/2 Inches*

Modeller: Freda Doughty
Colourways: **A.** Red dress with white collar, cuffs and underdress; blue sash; blue hat with yellow band; yellow shoe
              B. Rose-pink dress with white collar, cuffs and underdress; green sash; shoe
Backstamp: Black

R.W. No.	Backstamp	Height	Intro.	Discon.	Current Market Value U.K. £	U.S.$	Can. $
3547B	B-4	9 1/2"	1955	1958	450.00	700.00	950.00

3569   *THE SEAMSTRESS*

Modeller: Freda Doughty
Colourways: **A.** Blue dress; blue and rose fabrics
  B. Red dress; multi-coloured fabrics

Backstamp: Black

R.W. No.	Backstamp	Height	Intro.	Discon.	Current Market Value		
					U.K. £	U.S.$	Can. $
3569	B-4	6"	1956	1959	350.00	525.00	725.00

SERIES: *Alice in Wonderland*

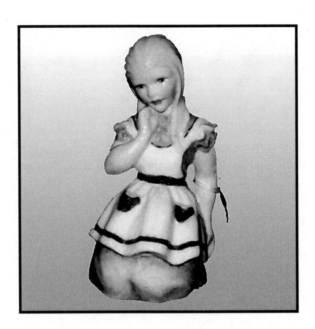

Modeller: Freda Doughty
Colourways: Pale blue dress; white apron trimmed with rose-pink; yellow hair
Backstamp: Black

R.W. No.	Backstamp	Height	Intro.	Discon.	Current Market Value U.K. £	U.S.$	Can. $
3608	B-4	4"	1957	1959	500.00	775.00	950.00

_3609_   **_CHESHIRE CAT_**

SERIES: *Alice in Wonderland*

Modeller: Freda Doughty
Colourways: **A.** Grey with white markings
                B. White

Backstamp: Black

R.W. No.	Backstamp	Height	Intro.	Discon.	Current Market Value		
					U.K. £	U.S.$	Can. $
3609	B-4	3 1/2"	1957	1959	600.00	925.00	1,250.00

3610   MOCK TURTLE

SERIES: *Alice in Wonderland*

Modeller: Freda Doughty
Colourways: Brown head; green fins; yellow shell

Backstamp: Black

R.W. No.	Backstamp	Height	Intro.	Discon.	Current Market Value		
					U.K. £	U.S.$	Can. $
3610	B-4	3 1/4"	1957	1959	500.00	775.00	950.00

3611   WHITE RABBIT

SERIES: *Alice in Wonderland*

Modeller: Freda Doughty
Colourways: **A.** Red coat; yellow waistcoat with black buttons, black bow-tie; white gloves
            B. White
Backstamp: Black

R.W. No.	Backstamp	Height	Intro.	Discon.	Current Market Value U.K. £	U.S.$	Can. $
3611	B-4	4"	1957	1959	600.00	925.00	1,250.00

3612   *THE DUCHESS*

SERIES: *Alice in Wonderland*

Modeller: Freda Doughty
Colourways: Purple robe trimmed in yellow; yellow dress; purple headdress; white veil
Backstamp: Black

R.W. No.	Backstamp	Height	Intro.	Discon.	Current Market Value		
					U.K. £	U.S.$	Can. $
3612	B-4	4"	1957	1959	550.00	850.00	1,000.00

3613   **THE DODO**

Modeller: Freda Doughty
Colourways: **A.** Brown back; yellow breast; cream and yellow face; red eyes, beak and feet; brown cane
                        B. Pale brown back; yellow breast; pale green and yellow face; blue cuffs; pink eyes, beak and feet;
                        pale brown cane

Backstamp: Black

R.W. No.	Backstamp	Height	Intro.	Discon.	Current Market Value U.K. £	U.S.$	Can. $
3613	B-4	3 1/4"	1957	1959	450.00	700.00	950.00

3614   *FATHER WILLIAM*

SERIES: *Alice in Wonderland*

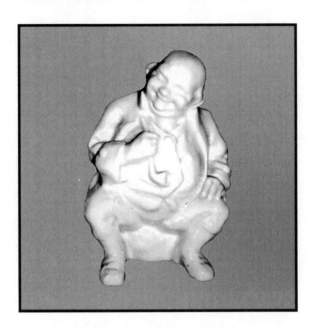

Modeller: Freda Doughty
Colourways: **A.** Blue coat; yellow waistcoat with blue buttons; brown trousers; red cravat; white hair and pipe
           B. White
Backstamp: Black

R.W. No.	Backstamp	Height	Intro.	Discon.	Current Market Value U.K. £	U.S.$	Can. $
3614	B-4	3 1/4"	1957	1959	500.00	775.00	950.00

3615

LONG-HAIRED CAT

Modeller: Freda Doughty
Colourways: Grey and white

Backstamp: Black

R.W. No.	Backstamp	Height	Intro.	Discon.	Current Market Value		
					U.K. £	U.S.$	Can. $
3615	B-4	3 1/2"	1957	1959	150.00	250.00	300.00

3616   *SHORT-HAIRED CAT*

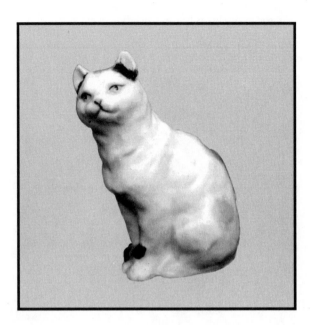

Modeller: Freda Doughty
Colourways: White with brown markings

Backstamp: Black

R.W. No.	Backstamp	Height	Intro.	Discon.	Current Market Value		
					U.K. £	U.S.$	Can. $
3616	B-4	3"	1957	1959	150.00	250.00	300.00

3629 *FIRST DANCE*

First discontinued in 1980, this model was reintroduced in 1990.

Modeller: Freda Doughty
Colourways: A. Cream dress; burgundy stole with black fringe
                B. Cream dress with yellow highlights; yellow stole with gold fringe
                C. Mauve dress; pink stole with yellow and blue edging and black fringe
Backstamp: Black

R.W. No.	Backstamp	Height	Intro.	Discon.	Current Market Value U.K. £	U.S.$	Can. $
3629	B-4	7"	1957	1961	125.00	200.00	250.00
3629	B-5	7"	1962	1980	100.00	150.00	200.00
3629	B-6	7"	1990	Current	80.00	125.00	175.00

3630 *SWEET ANNE*

Modeller: Freda Doughty
Colourways: **A.** Blue dress with white cuffs and underskirt; light brown hair; green fan; gloss
B. Mottled green and lilac dress; gloss
C. Pale green dress with white cuffs and underskirt; multi-coloured fan; light brown hair; matte
Backstamp: Black

R.W. No.	Backstamp	Height	Intro.	Discon.	Current Market Value		
					U.K. £	U.S.$	Can. $
3630	B-4	7 1/2"	1957	1961	125.00	200.00	250.00
3630	B-5	7 1/2"	1962	1985	80.00	125.00	175.00

3638 *WEDNESDAY'S CHILD — GIRL*

First discontinued in 1957, this model was reintroduced in 1994.

STYLE TWO: *Seated girl with dog*

Modeller: Freda Doughty
Colourways: Pink dress with white collar; brown hair; brown dog; grey rock; green and yellow base
Backstamp: Black

R.W. No.	Backstamp	Height	Intro.	Discon.	Current Market Value		
					U.K. £	U.S.$	Can. $
3638	B-4	Unknown	1957	1957		Rare	
3638	B-6	Unknown	1994	Current	85.00	125.00	175.00

3654 **SPANISH BEAUTY**

*Photograph not available
at press time*

Modeller: Freda Doughty
Colourways: Unknown
Backstamp: Black

R.W. No.	Backstamp	Height	Intro.	Discon.	Current Market Value		
					U.K. £	U.S.$	Can. $
3654	B-4	Unknown	1958	1958		Rare	

3655   *SURPRISE*

Modeller: Freda Doughty
Colourways: Yellow dress; pink and green sash; brown hair

Backstamp: Black

R.W. No.	Backstamp	Height	Intro.	Discon.	Current Market Value		
					U.K. £	U.S.$	Can. $
3655	B-4	7 1/2"	1958	1958	600.00	925.00	1,250.00

3656   **MAYFLOWER**

For style two see shape number 3761.

STYLE ONE: *With Hat And Telescope*

Modeller: Freda Doughty
Colourways: Red jacket with yellow buttons; yellow waistcoat; pale green breeches; black bow, shoes and hat;
light brown ship with yellow sails

Backstamp: Black

R.W. No.	Backstamp	Height	Intro.	Discon.	Current Market Value		
					U.K. £	U.S.$	Can. $
3656	B-4	7 1/2"	1958	1958	600.00	925.00	1,250.00

3679 FALCONER

Modeller: Freda Doughty
Colourways: Cream shirt; beige and maroon doublet; brown shoes; dark brown and golden eagle
Backstamp: Black

R.W. No.	Backstamp	Height	Intro.	Discon.	Current Market Value U.K. £	U.S.$	Can. $
3679	B-4	7"	1959	1959	800.00	1,250.00	1,500.00

3698

INVITATION

*Photograph not available
at press time*

Modeller: Freda Doughty
Colourways: Unknown

Backstamp: Black

R.W. No.	Backstamp	Height	Intro.	Discon.	Current Market Value		
					U.K. £	U.S.$	Can. $
3698	B-4	8 1/4"	1960	1960		Rare	

3699   *RED RIBBONS*

Photograph not available
at press time

Modeller: Freda Doughty
Colourways: Unknown

Backstamp: Black

R.W. No.	Backstamp	Height	Intro.	Discon.	Current Market Value U.K. £	U.S.$	Can. $
3699	B-4	Unknown	1960	1960		Rare	

3714 *SIAMESE CAT*

Photograph not available
at press time

Modeller: Freda Doughty
Colourways: Unknown

Backstamp: Black

R.W. No.	Backstamp	Height	Intro.	Discon.	Current Market Value U.K. £	U.S.$	Can. $
3714	B-4	Unknown	1961	1961	Not issued		

3720

WILL YOU, WON'T YOU?

*Photograph not available
at press time*

Modeller: Freda Doughty
Colourways: Unknown
Backstamp: Black

R.W. No.	Backstamp	Height	Intro.	Discon.	Current Market Value U.K. £	U.S.$	Can. $
3720	B-4	Unknown	1961	1961		Rare	

3760   *FANTAILS*

The model November (3418) was redesigned in 1963 and named Fantails see page 67.

Modeller: Freda Doughty
Colourways: White coat with lilac highlights; blue leggings; blue cap trimmed with white; three white doves
Backstamp: Black

R.W. No.	Backstamp	Height	Intro.	Discon.	Current Market Value U.K. £	U.S.$	Can. $
3760	B-5	7 1/4"	1963	c.1982	225.00	350.00	475.00

3761   MAYFLOWER

This model of Mayflower, without a hat or telescope on the base, was altered to help boost sales. For style one see shape number 3656.

STYLE TWO: *Without Hat and Telescope*

Modeller: Freda Doughty
Colourways: Blue jacket with yellow buttons; pale yellow epaulettes and waistcoat; beige breeches; black bow and shoes; brown ship with white sails
Backstamp: Black

R.W. No.	Backstamp	Height	Intro.	Discon.	Current Market Value U.K. £	U.S.$	Can. $
3761	B-5	7 1/2"	1963	1963	600.00	925.00	1,250.00

INDEX

**ANTIQUE REFERENCE
BOOKS AVAILABLE**

DAVID ALDOUS-COOK

P.O. BOX 413, SUTTON,
SURREY SM3 8SZ
UNITED KINGDOM
TEL./FAX: 0181-642-4842

MARNALEA ANTIQUES

**THE FIGURINE SPECIALIST
SERVING COLLECTORS SINCE 1974!**

**We Carry
One of Canada's Largest Collections of
DISCONTINUED ROYAL DOULTON &
ROYAL WORCESTER**

*FIGURINES · JUGS · ANIMALS · PLATES
SERIESWARE · LAMBETH · ROYAL WORCESTER*

MAILING LIST AVAILABLE
Our Selection's Great - Our Prices Competitive -
And The GST Is Always Included!

**51 MAIN STREET NORTH,
CAMPBELLVILLE, ONTARIO L0P 1B0**
TEL: 905 854 0287 FAX: 905 854 3117
e-mail: AJKREVER@aol.com

Cross & Cross
Collectibles

Buyers and Sellers of Fine Collectibles
No Collection Too Large or Too Small
We Ship World Wide
Send For Our Latest Price List

1-800-769-8330 in Canada or the U.S.

1-416-516-8800 For International Calls

Visit us at crosscross@globalserve.net

253 College St, Suite 159, Toronto, Ontario, M5T 1R5

124

WILLIAM CROSS
Antiques & Collectibles Inc.

ROYAL
WORCESTER
FIGURINES

We Fill Want Lists
Lowest Prices Guaranteed!

Worldwide Delivery

Call or Send for Current List:

4631 East Hastings
Burnaby, B.C. V5C 2K6
Tel: (604) 298-9599
Fax: (604) 298-9563
Outside B.C.: 1-800-639-7771

ATTENTION
ROYAL WORCESTER
COLLECTORS

I am currently seeking
historical information on
Royal Worcester

If you have old catalogues, advertising
pamphlets, promotional literature, or
other items pertaining to Royal
Worcester products I am interested in
purchasing them.
If you have an interesting porcelain
figurine collection in the period 1900 to
present I would like to photograph it.

Please contact:
Tony Cast
Phone: 01943 874975 (U.K.)

Colonial House of Collectibles & Santa's North Pole World

ROYAL
DOULTON
IS OUR
SPECIALTY!
We Buy
We Sell
We Appraise

Colonial House Features the Largest Selection of Current and Discontinued Items in the Following Lines:

- OLD & NEW ROYAL DOULTON
- FIGURES AND CHARACTER JUGS
- HUMMELS
- DAVID WINTER COTTAGES
- WALT DISNEY CLASSICS
- DEPT.56 COTTAGES AND
  SNOWBABIES
- BELLEEK
- ROYAL WORCESTER

- WEE FOREST FOLK
- PRECIOUS MOMENTS
- LILLIPUT LANE
- BOSSONS WALL ORNAMENTS
- SWAROVSKI CRYSTAL
- LLADRO
- DUNCAN ROYALE
- B & G AND R.C.

Send for our latest product catalogue

WE DO MAIL ORDERS

COLONIAL HOUSE ANTIQUES & GIFTS
182 Front Street, Berea, Ohio 44017; 216-826-4169 or 1-800-344-9299; Fax 216-826-0839
Monday to Saturday 10 a.m. to 5 p.m. Or by Appointment

Alexandra Antiques

The Tything, Worcester
(Opposite Grammar School)

FOR A GOOD SELECTION OF PORCELAIN
JEWELLERY, CERAMICS, CLOCKS.
EXCELLENT STOCK OF <u>WORCESTER PORCELAIN</u>
INCLUDING IMPORTANT PIECES,
ANTIQUE FURNITURE AND MUCH MORE!

TRADE   **01905 723322**   WELCOME

WALSALL
ANTIQUES
CENTRE

A JEWEL IN
THE HEART
OF WALSALL

2 Miles from the M 6 Motorway

Many dealers displaying an exceptional array of porcelain and pottery, jewellery, glassware, silver, metalware, antique furniture and much more.

MONDAY to SATURDAY 10am to 5pm

WALSALL ANTIQUES CENTRE
Digbeth Arcade, Walsall, England WS1 1RE
Telephone: 01922 725163

BYGONES
OF WORCESTER

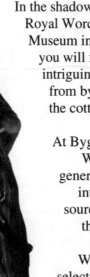

In the shadow of the Cathedral and close to the Royal Worcester Porcelain Factory and Museum in the "Faithful City" of Worcester you will find two shops packed with an intriguing variety of antiques and items from bygone days which have graced the cottages and castles of yesteryear.

At Bygones we have been dealing in Worcester china for three generations, and are recognized internationally as a leading source of Worcester dating from the 1750s to the present day.

We always have a wide selection of Worcester figures in stock, particularly the scarcer models and pieces in perfect unrestored condition.

Suppliers to Museums, Collectors and Dealers throughout the world.

Gabrielle Doherty Bullock F.G.A
55 Sidbury and Cathedral Square, Worcester, United Kingdom.
Telephone and Fax (01905) 25388 and 23132

We are always interested in purchasing Worcester Figures and offer free advice, a fair price and immediate payment.

127

The Charlton Standards

THE CHARLTON
STANDARD CATALOGUE OF
**ROYAL DOULTON
BESWICK JUGS**
THIRD EDITION

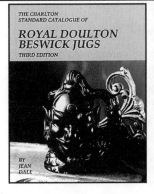

Royal Doulton Beswick Jugs
3rd Edition, by Jean Dale
The most comprehensive guide to Royal Doulton and
Beswick jugs. Over 500 listings.
632 pages; 7" x 9"; softcover;
$24.95 Cdn., $19.95 U.S., £16.95 U.K.
ISBN 0-88968-166-X

THE CHARLTON
STANDARD CATALOGUE OF
**BESWICK
ANIMALS**

2nd Edition

**Available from
your favourite
dealer or
bookstore, or by
calling the
Charlton Press
on our toll free
lines from
Canada or the
U.S.**

Beswick Animals
**2nd Edition, by Diana & John Callow and
Marilyn & Peter Sweet**
An indispensable guide for Beswick
collectors. Over 800 photographs.
488 pages; 7" x 9"; softcover;
$24.95 Cdn., $19.95 U.S., £16.95 U.K.
ISBN 0-88968-177-5

THE CHARLTON
STANDARD CATALOGUE OF
**ROYAL DOULTON
BESWICK STORYBOOK
FIGURINES**

BY
JEAN
DALE

THIRD
EDITION

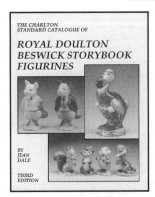

**FOR TOLL
FREE
ORDERING**
Call
1-800-442-6042
Fax
1-800-442-1542

Royal Doulton Beswick
Storybook Figurines
3rd Edition, by Jean Dale
From Alice in Wonderland to Winnie the
Pooh, this illustrated catalogue contains over
375 photographs.
275 pages; 7" x 9"; softcover;
$19.95 Cdn., $17.95 U.S., £14.95 U.K.
ISBN 0-88968-163-5

THE CHARLTON
STANDARD CATALOGUE OF
WADE
WHIMSICAL
COLLECTABLES

BY
PAT
MURRAY

THIRD
EDITION

Wade Whimsical Collectables
3rd Edition, by Pat Murray
Explore Wade's whimsical world. More than 350 photographs.
216 pages; 7" x 9"; softcover;
$19.95 Cdn., $17.50 U.S., £14.95 U.K.
ISBN 0-88968-173-6

The Charlton Press

2040 Yonge St., Suite 208, Toronto,
Ontario, Canada M4S 1Z9

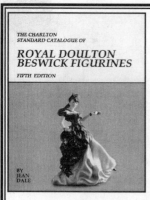

THE CHARLTON
STANDARD CATALOGUE OF

ROYAL DOULTON BESWICK FIGURINES

FIFTH EDITION

BY JEAN DALE

The Charlton Standards

Royal Doulton Beswick Figurines
5th Edition, by Jean Dale
The most authorative source for all Royal Doulton figurines. Over 3,000 models are listed, priced and illustrated.
444 pages; 7" x 9"; softcover;
$24.95 Cdn., $19.95 U.S., £16.95 U.K.
ISBN 0-88968-161-9

Available from your favourite dealer or bookstore, or by calling the Charlton Press on our toll free lines from Canada or the U.S.

THE CHARLTON
STANDARD CATALOGUE OF

WADE

By PAT MURRAY

VOLUME ONE
General Issues

2nd EDITION

Wade, Volume 1–General Issues
2nd Edition, by Pat Murray
From animals to tankards, from figures to commemorative ware, it's all here in the most comprehensive catalogue on Wade.
411 pages; 7" x 9"; softcover;
$24.95 Cdn., $19.95 U.S., £16.95 U.K.
ISBN 0-88968-139-2

Wade, Volume 2–Decorative Ware
2nd Edition, by Pat Murray
For the first time all Wade's flowers, plaques, vases, pots, decorative dishes and more are assembled in one convenient volume.
300 pages; 7" x 9"; softcover;
$24.95 Cdn., $19.95 U.S., £16.95 U.K.
ISBN 0-88968-181-3

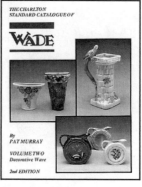

THE CHARLTON
STANDARD CATALOGUE OF

WADE

By PAT MURRAY

VOLUME TWO
Decorative Ware

2nd EDITION

FOR TOLL FREE ORDERING
Call
1-800-442-6042
Fax
1-800-442-1542

Chintz
1st Edition, by Linda Eberle and Susan Scott
This eagerly awaited Chintz pricing catalogue covers all major and minor producers of Chintzware.
190 pages; 7" x 9"; softcover;
$19.95 Cdn., $17.95 U.S., £14.95 U.K.
ISBN 0-88968-179-1

The Charlton Standard Catalogue of

CHINTZ

FIRST EDITION

The Charlton Press

2040 Yonge St., Suite 208, Toronto,
Ontario, Canada M4S 1Z9